ART
FOR THE HEART

Nia miraku

WELBECK

Published in 2022 by Welbeck Children's Books
Part of Welbeck Publishing Group
20 Mortimer Street, London W1T 3JW

A CIP catalogue record for this book
is available from the British Library.

ISBN 978 1 78312 762 7

Printed in Heshan, China

10 9 8 7 6 5 4 3 2 1

Author and illustrator: Xavier Leopold
Consultant: Sarah Davis
Design Manager: Matt Drew
Editorial Manager: Joff Brown
Production: Melanie Robertson

PICTURE CREDITS:
Erik Svoboda/Shutterstock.com,
Carabus/Shutterstock.com,
Lovely Mandala/Shutterstock.com

FSC
www.fsc.org
MIX
Paper from
responsible sources
FSC® C020056

Xavier Leopold

Xviart

ART
FOR THE HEART

A fill-in art journal
for a happy, confident you!

CONTENTS

Hi!
I'M XAVI
Welcome to my book!

My name's Xavi and I'm an artist... but I only picked up a brush for the first time in 2020! I didn't have any training in art, but I knew I wanted to express myself. Soon, I was creating paintings which showed everyone how I was feeling. Before long, my art was hanging on people's walls, and I was even exhibiting my art in galleries!

But best of all, making art really helped feel me better. It let me express my emotions and got me through some tough times. Art really is for the heart – everyone should be able to make the art they love.

Making
ART FOR THE HEART

 Art doesn't have to be perfect.

 It doesn't have to follow rules.

 It doesn't have to be made by 'artists'.

It just has to be something YOU love making!

YOU can make art that expresses how you feel, what you love, and what you want to say about the world.

It might be drawing, painting, model making, or anything else. **MAKING ART MAKES YOU FEEL GOOD.** It can help you work out how you feel, or let other people know how you feel. It can energise you, comfort you, or help you feel calm.

This book is full of cool activities to get you drawing and painting **YOUR** way. So if you've ever wanted to make some cool art, but didn't know where to start, this book is for you!

How to use
THIS BOOK

Why not start right now and color this in?

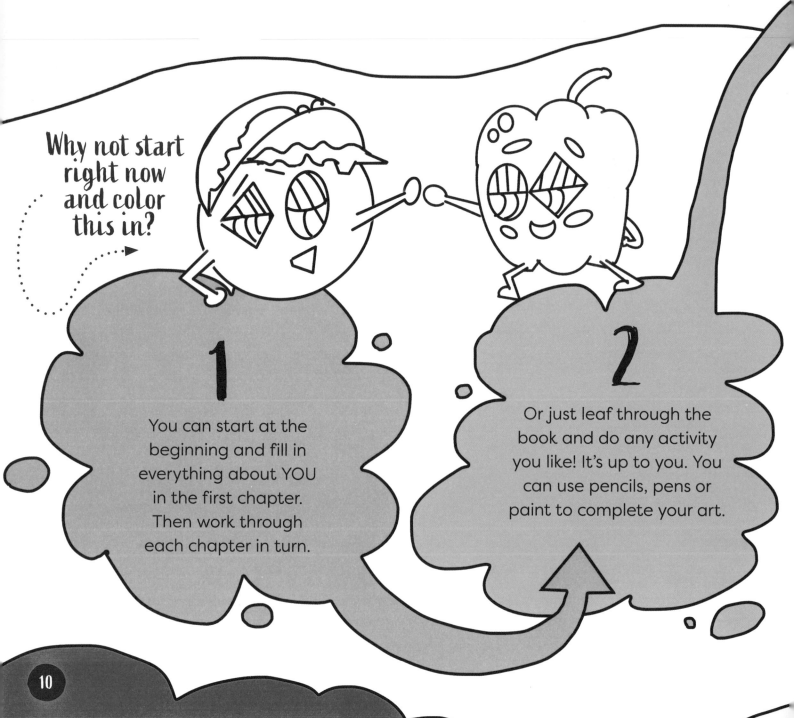

1

You can start at the beginning and fill in everything about YOU in the first chapter. Then work through each chapter in turn.

2

Or just leaf through the book and do any activity you like! It's up to you. You can use pencils, pens or paint to complete your art.

3

Every activity is just a
starting point. If you want
to do any of the activities in
your own way, then do it!

4

You don't have to draw or
paint in the book - you can
trace any shapes onto a
separate piece of paper, and
work on them separately.

...why not colour
him in too!

Just have fun, be creative
and get your art on!

Join in
ONLINE!

See Xavi in action! On the Xavi Art Club Youtube channel, you'll find lots of fun videos to get you creating your own cool art.

Watch Xavi paint his own amazing art!

Find out how Xavi drew the pictures in this book!

Step 1

Step 2

Step 3

Watch Xavi create his art in time-lapse videos!

Step 4

Step 5

Step 6

Get even more tips on how making your own art can help you stay happy and motivated!

THE XAVI ART CLUB PLAYLIST IS AT
YOUTUBE.COM/WELBECKPUBLISHINGGROUP

PART 1

ALL ABOUT YOU

WHAT MAKES YOU – YOU?

Use these pages to write and draw everything about YOU. What you look like – your friends and family – where you live and where you go to school.

Don't forget to put in everything you like – all the sports, books, games and TV shows that fill up your brain. This is your space to say what really makes you special!

THIS IS ME!

Draw yourself in the outline shape wearing your favourite clothes, and fill in the details about yourself on the sheet too.

My hairstyle

My name:
....

Nicknames:
....
....

(But I hate being called):
....

I have ☐ brothers

and ☐ sisters

If I could, I would wear
....
....
                    every day!

I was born on
....

Which makes me
....

years old

I'm amazing at:
....
....

And I want to learn how to:
....
....

Favourite shoes

THINGS I LOVE

Whay people, subjects, games, books, sports or TV
are filling up your thoughts right now? Draw it all!

People
Who are you thinking
about? They can be real
or from fiction!

Games
Do you have a favourite
videogame (or even a board
game)? Draw it here!

TV & Movies
Draw a favourite film, star or a scene.

Sport
Draw sports or hobbies you
like to play or watch.

"I STAY TRUE TO MYSELF AND MY STYLE, AND I AM ALWAYS PUSHING MYSELF TO BE AWARE OF THAT AND BE ORIGINAL."

AALIYAH
Singer

MY V.I.P.s

Fill these frames with the Very Important People
in your life - friends, family, even pets!

Name: ....

Important because:

....

....

Name: ....

Important because:

....

....

Name: ....

Important because:

....

....

Name: ....

Important because:

....

....

Name: ....

Important because:

....

....

MY WORLD

Make a map of where you live, where you go to school, where your friends and family are, and maybe even places you like that are far away.

You can choose to make your map look as close to the real world as possible, or you can place things wherever you like. Just have fun with it!

Do you have relatives you see sometimes? Add where they live!

Don't forget to add your school.

Draw the places where you play or hang out.

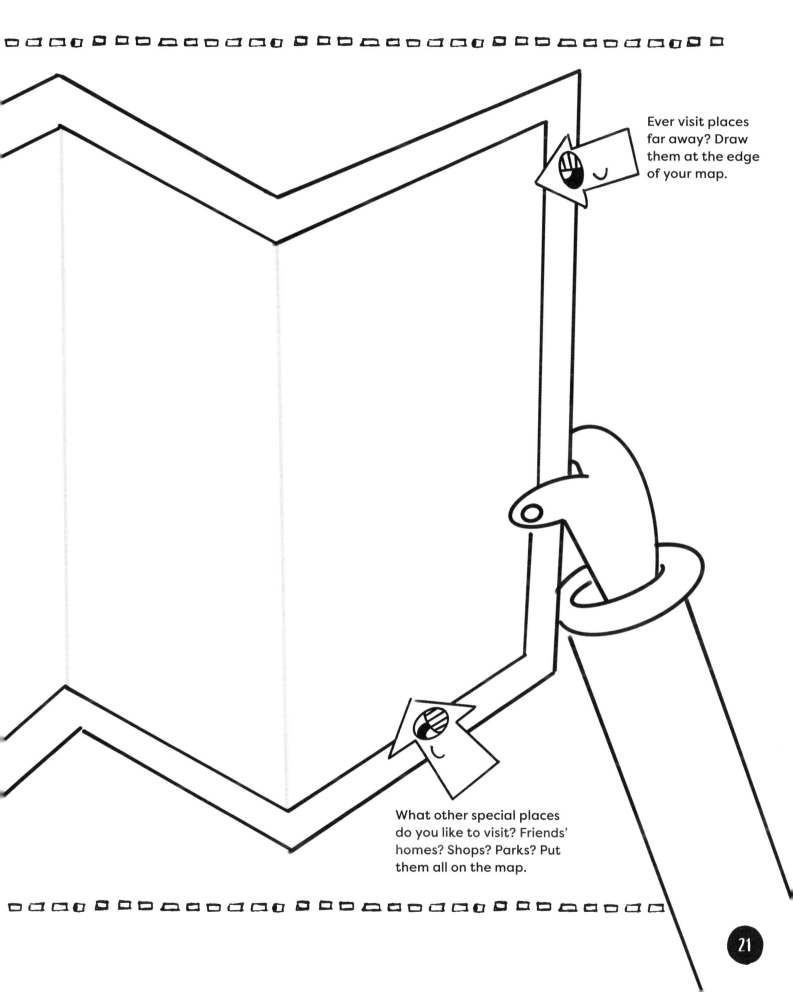

Ever visit places far away? Draw them at the edge of your map.

What other special places do you like to visit? Friends' homes? Shops? Parks? Put them all on the map.

ANIMAL ENERGY

What animal do you think you're most like?
Draw yourself as your animal.

MY ULTIMATE TEAM

You're putting together the ultimate superhero squad. Draw the real-life people you'd choose! They could be friends, family or your own personal heroes.

The muscle	The brains	The bravest	The leader... YOU!
Name:	Name:	Name:	Name:
H	E	R	O

THERE'S ONLY ONE YOU

Just think - everything you love, everything you do, everyone you know, makes you 100% UNIQUE. There's nobody in the world exactly like you!

WHY NOT TRY...

Make a list of all the things you can do this year, that you couldn't do last year. It could be schoolwork, sports skills or tricks, new words you've learned, new food you've tried, new people you've met... you might be surprised how much you've changed!

PART 2

THINK POSITIVE

MAKING ART MAKES YOU FEEL GOOD

Creating art can help you bring out positive feelings -
whether it's doodling, drawing, painting, writing or making music.
Remember, only YOU can create your own art - nobody else
can do it just like you. Try these activities to bring
some sunshine to your day!

POSITIVE

BEST DAY EVER

What was your best day ever?
Draw it here!

It might be when you did something new for the first time...

MY BEST EVER CAKE!

Or when you achieved something that was special to you.

BEST DAY STILL TO COME!

Now think of something amazing that you'd
love to happen, one day in the future.

Perhaps it's
winning a
match...

...or visiting
somewhere
completely new.

"IF EVERYTHING WAS PERFECT, YOU WOULD NEVER LEARN AND YOU WOULD NEVER GROW"

BEYONCÉ KNOWLES
Singer-songwriter and actress

MY MEDALS

Give yourself some medals for good stuff you've done. It could be for helping others, being brave in tough times, or for skills you've learned.

Award for:

Award for:

Award for:

Award for:

POSITIVE COMICS!

Got a problem that's getting you down? Draw a comic strip of it here, where you manage to solve it. It could be a serious or silly solution!

Now you try. Write and draw your problem here

IT HAPPENED TO ME!

Little things can make you just as happy as big ones. Write or draw four awesome things that you have experienced recently. It could be a great meal, a hug, a new song, an amazing movie, or fun with friends.

1

2

3

4

PAY IT FORWARD

Now it's time to think about making a positive difference to other people around you. Draw four of your friends or family, and write down something positive to say to them that you've never told them before.

What I'd tell them:
....
....
....

Name:
....

What I'd tell them:
....
....
....

Name:
....

What I'd tell them:
....
....
....

Name:
....

What I'd tell them:
....
....
....

Name:
....

Now for the hard bit - go and tell them all! You might be surprised at how glad they are to hear it.

BELIEVE IN YOURSELF!

Whenever you're feeling down, try to think of people you love, peaceful scenes, or a time you felt really happy. You'll be suprised how much it helps!

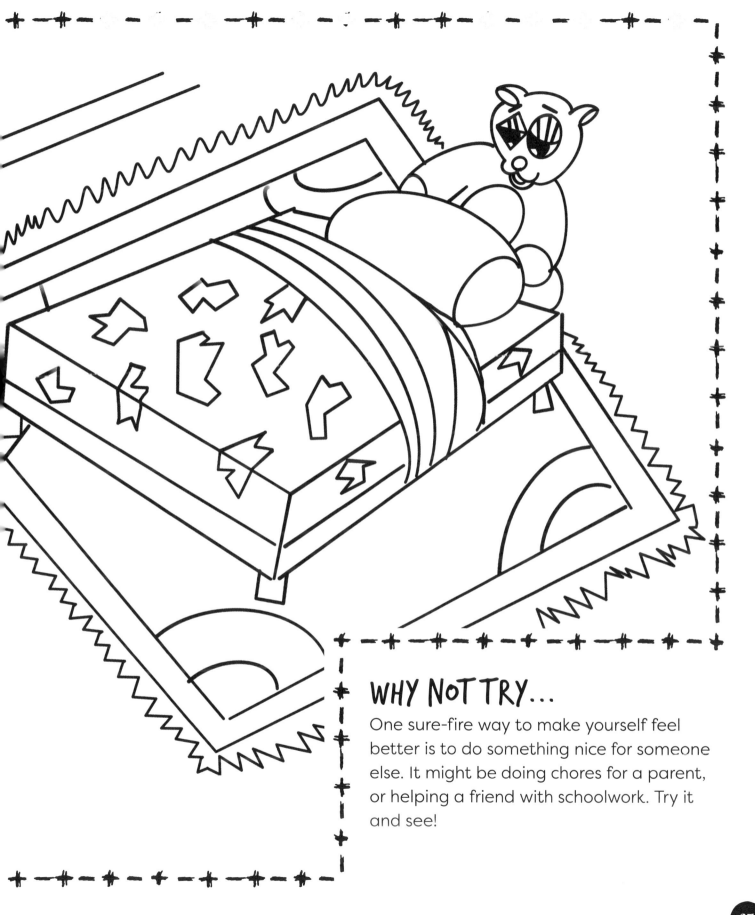

WHY NOT TRY...

One sure-fire way to make yourself feel better is to do something nice for someone else. It might be doing chores for a parent, or helping a friend with schoolwork. Try it and see!

PART 3

LIVE WELL

YOU ARE WHAT YOU EAT!

...which is why you're a chicken nugget. Well, maybe not! But it's true that you can make yourself feel so much better if you eat nutritious food and get plenty of fresh air and sun. So why not draw it all out?

MY GREAT PLATE

Draw all your favourite food as part of this amazing spread.

YUM!

DELICIOUS!

UURRGHHH!

Now draw a plate of the food you **HATE**!
Make it as gross as you can!

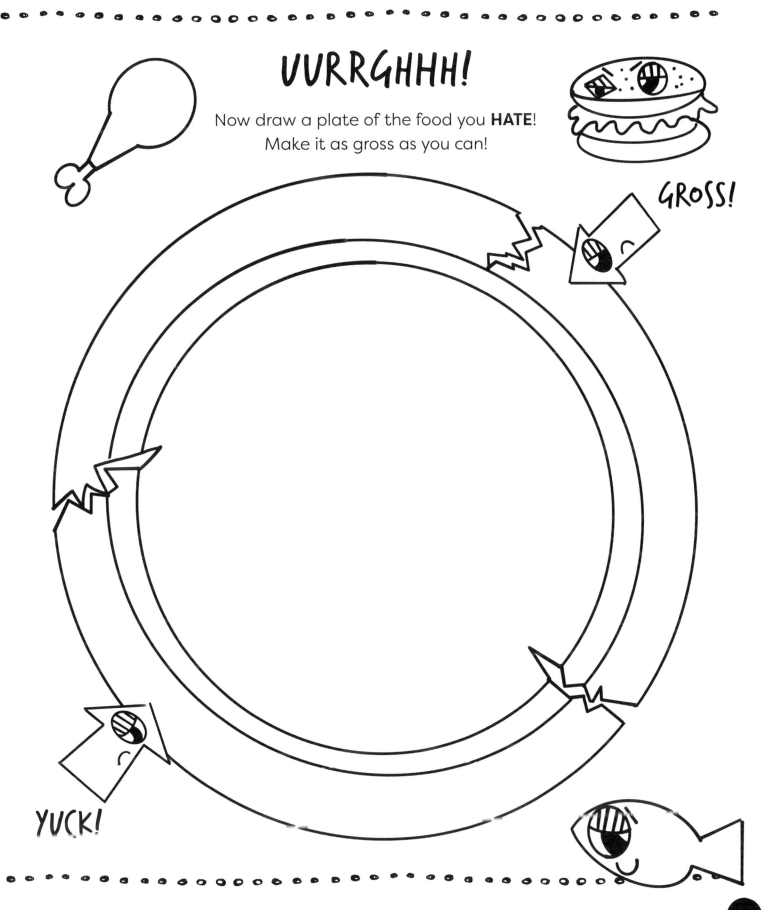

GROSS!

YUCK!

"Laughter is brightest where food is best"

IRISH PROVERB

EAT THE RAINBOW

Have you heard the phrase 'eat the rainbow'? It means that it's good to eat a whole bunch of different fruit and veg, featuring many different colours. Fill in this list, ticking off and colouring in the ones you've eaten recently. Can you complete the rainbow?

RED

YELLOW

ORANGE

GREEN

BLUE

PURPLE

Other fruit and veg I love:

....

....

....

....

FOOD FIGHT!

Here are a bunch of less healthy foods, about to have a battle with some healthy food heroes! Can you add some more foods, and get them fighting? Let battle commence!

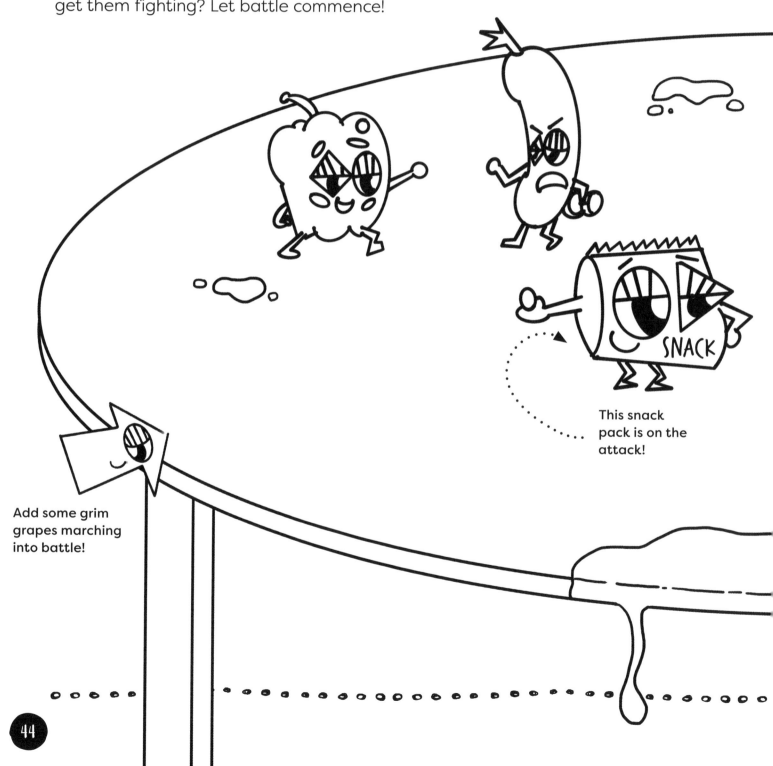

This snack pack is on the attack!

Add some grim grapes marching into battle!

Draw some food flying through the air to attack!

DON'T WORRY...

There's really no such thing as 'bad food'! As long as you eat lots of fruit and veg, you can enjoy any food in moderation. Just don't eat TOO MUCH of the less healthy stuff!

Where will this drink's sugary shot land?

This milk has gone bad!

5-A-DAY CHALLENGE

Make a note of the fruit and veg that you eat every day for a week.
Try and eat at least five portions a day - more if you can. Draw or
write them here and then add up your points for the week!

Bonus veg!

Monday						
Tuesday						
Wednesday						
Thursday						
Friday						
Saturday						
Sunday						

I ate ☐ fruit and veg this week

FOOD QUIZ

Find out what kind of eater you are by answering these questions!

1. You're late for school, so you grab a snack. Is it:

- [ ] A) An apple
- [ ] B) Toast with jam
- [ ] C) A giant-sized chocolate bar

2. At birthday parties, I like to fill my plate with:

- [ ] A) Carrot sticks and dips
- [ ] B) A good handful of crisps to go with my sandwich
- [ ] C) Dessert, dessert and more dessert!

3. My idea of eating lots of different food is:

- [ ] A) Eating the rainbow of fruits and veggies
- [ ] B) Beans, waffles and sausages
- [ ] C) Chips, mash AND potato wedges!

4. An adult offers you an unusual-looking new food to try. "It's delicious!" they say. Do you:

- [ ] A) Grab it and bite in straight away!
- [ ] B) Sniff it and nibble it delicately
- [ ] C) Shout 'URGH URGH NO' and run off at top speed

5. My favourite sweet treat is:

- [ ] A) A massive fruit salad
- [ ] B) A big bowl of popcorn
- [ ] C) Anything that's deep-fried and covered in sugar, sauce and sprinkles!

ANSWERS

MOSTLY A: Congrats - sounds like you're a super healthy eater! Keep it up!

MOSTLY B: Like most people, you love a less healthy snack sometimes! No problem as long as it's not too often, and you make sure you get those veggies on your plate!

MOSTLY C: Maybe it's time to cut back on fatty and sugary foods, and eat more fruit and veg - you'll be amazed how much better it makes you feel!

ENJOY YOUR FOOD!

Remember - food is one of the best things in life! The more different food you eat, and the more fruit and veg you can include, the better you'll feel!

WHY NOT TRY...

You and a friend could try a FOOD SWAP CHALLENGE, where you both eat something the other person loves, but you hate! Your taste changes, over time, so if you haven't eaten something for a while... you might find you love it now!

PART 4

GET ACTIVE

MOVE YOUR BODY, IMPROVE YOUR MIND!

Did you know that exercise helps you achieve and maintain a healthy body? And if you're active now, then you are very likely to be super healthy as an adult!

Did you also know that exercise improves your way of thinking? If you ever feel nervous or anxious, a bit of exercise could help you shake it off.

MY SPORTS HERO

Draw or paint your ultimate sports hero here. Is it a famous sportsperson, or someone you know?

What do you think they'd say if you met them?

NAME:

....

SPORT:

....

SKILLS:

....

GREATEST WIN:

....

CHASE CHALLENGE

Fancy a challenge? Time yourself running a set distance (maybe the length of a street or a garden) and write down how long it takes.

Run three times a week, and write down your times. It doesn't matter how slow you are to begin with – if you can get faster, you're winning!

Write down your times here!

	Run 1	Run 2	Run 3
Week 1			
Week 2			
Week 3			
Week 4			

Miss a run or two? No worries, just carry on where you left off!

"Don't be AFRAID of FAILURE. This is the way to SUCCEED."

LEBRON JAMES
NBA basketball player

TOP TALENT

Come up with your own dance or fitness routine to make you a social media superstar! Fill in the four panels with four different moves to make up the routine.

Can you persuade your friends to do it with you in real life?

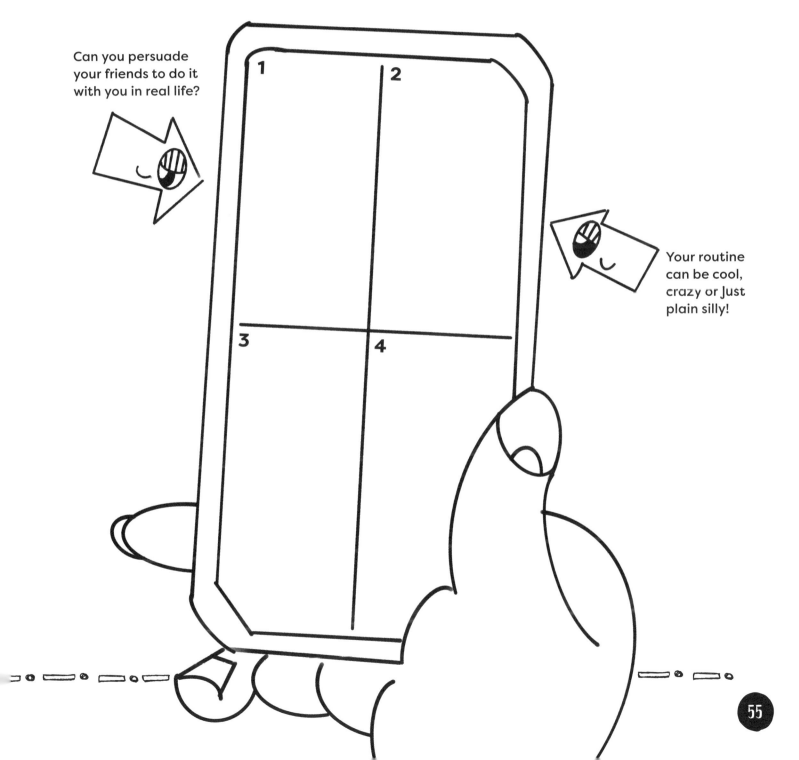

1

2

3

4

Your routine can be cool, crazy or just plain silly!

MAKE YOUR OWN SPORT

What crazy sport is taking place on this pitch?
Invent your own sport - maybe by combining
two different ones...

What will the goals
look like? Will they
move, float or
change size?

Does your sport
have a ball - or
more than one ball?
What shape is it?

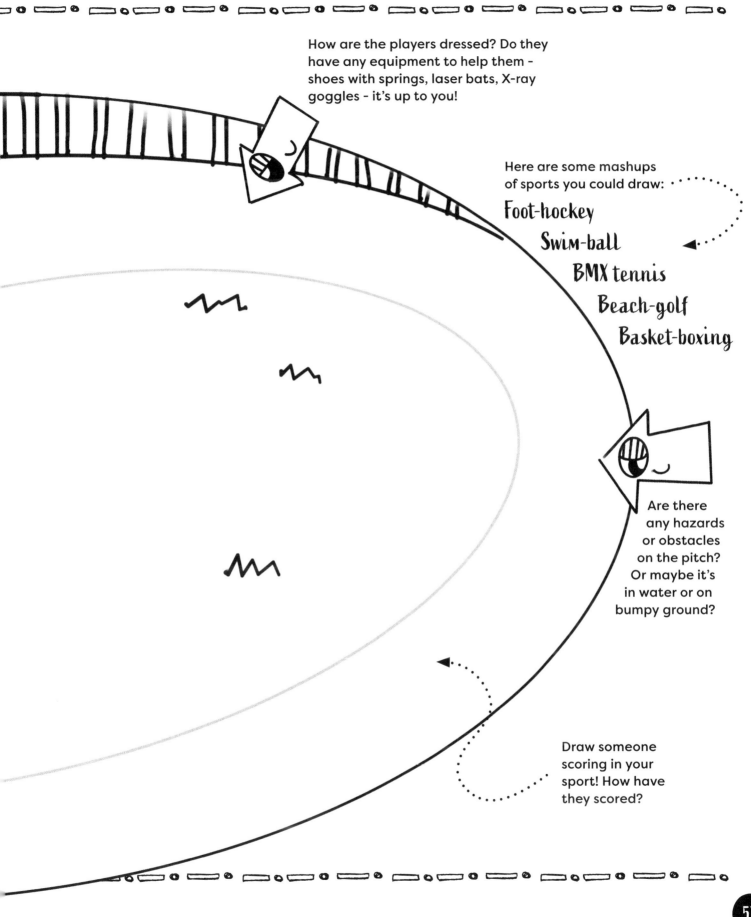

How are the players dressed? Do they have any equipment to help them - shoes with springs, laser bats, X-ray goggles - it's up to you!

Here are some mashups of sports you could draw:

Foot-hockey

Swim-ball

BMX tennis

Beach-golf

Basket-boxing

Are there any hazards or obstacles on the pitch? Or maybe it's in water or on bumpy ground?

Draw someone scoring in your sport! How have they scored?

KIT COMBO

Design your perfect sports kit here.

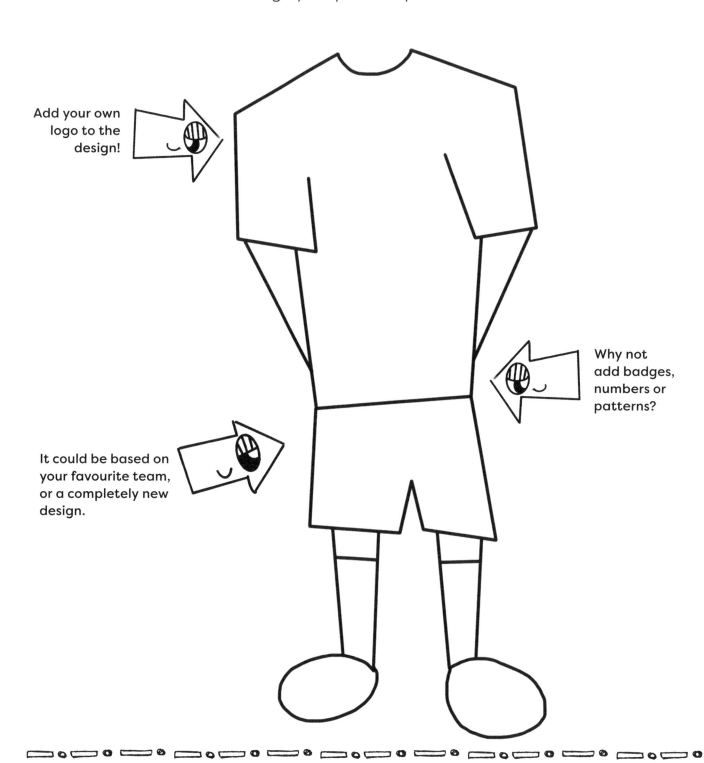

Add your own logo to the design!

Why not add badges, numbers or patterns?

It could be based on your favourite team, or a completely new design.

EXERCISE FLEX

Did you know that exercise gives you all these benefits? Circle the one you think is most important!

Okay, we added one in here that isn't real! Can you cross out the wrong one?

Lowers stress

Builds stronger heart, bones and muscles

2kg

Increases energy

Makes you fitter

Gives you time with friends

Improves concentration

Makes you fart louder

Lets you sleep better

Improves posture and balance

Improves self-esteem

10kg

The wrong one is 'Makes you fart louder'. Obviously!

GET MOVING!

It doesn't matter if it's a walk down the road or a super-intense sports session. Getting your body moving will help your mind, improve your health and give you confidence.

WHY NOT TRY...

The best way to keep fit is to do it with friends. Find a sport or activity your friends like and join a club... or maybe even start one.

PART 5

DO WHAT YOU LOVE

WHAT'S YOUR FAVOURITE THING?

Use this space to draw and write about your favourite books, movies and hobbies - and maybe find some new ones, too.

INSIDE...

Draw a pastime you love
doing indoors.

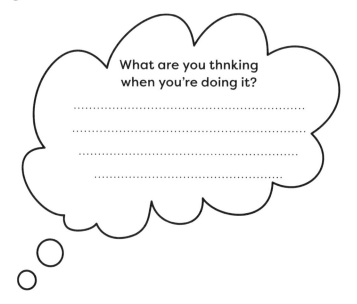

What are you thnking
when you're doing it?

....
....
....
....

**What room do
you do it in?**

**What equipment
do you need for it?**

..AND OUT

How about outside? Do you like cycling
or sports? Or exploring nature?

**What's the best thing
about your outdoor hobby?**

....

....

....

....

**What do you need for your
outdoor pastimes? A bike
or a ball, or just a sketch
pad? Draw it here!**

**Draw yourself in the clothes
you need for your activity.**

**Who do you do it with?
Friends or family? Or are
you part of a club?**

LOST IN A STORY

Imagine your favourite story from a book, movie, TV show or game. Now put yourself inside it. Who would you be - a character in the story, or yourself?

Charater Name:

....

Story title

....

In this story, I...

....

....

....

Add the story setting in the background.

Draw the other characters in the story. How would they react when they see you?

HOBBY PICKER

Rate the hobbies below, and whether
you've tried them or not.

Creative

Painting	/5
Drawing	/5
Filming	/5
Coding	/5
Building	/5

Add any other creative pastimes here:

....

I've never tried

....

But I will!

Social

Spending time with friends	/5
Using social media apps	/5
Going to family events	/5
Talking with friends online	/5
Joining clubs	/5

Add any other social pastimes here:

....

I've never tried

....

But I will!

Active

Football	/5
Swimming	/5
Cycling	/5
Basketball	/5
Martial Arts	/5

Add any other active pastimes here:

....

I've never tried

....

But I will!

Media

Watching movies	/5
Reading books	/5
Reading comics	/5
Playing games	/5
Watching online videos	/5

Add any other media pastimes here:

....

I've never tried

....

But I will!

THAT'S CRAZY!

These real-life hobbies are unsual, funny, dangerous
or just plain weird! Would you give any of them a try?

Extreme ironing

Yes, it's true! Some people compete to find
the craziest place to iron their clothes,
including up mountains or surfing!

Toy voyaging

In this hobby. you mail a fluffy toy off to
people around the world, who will take a photo
of your toy in all kinds of exotic locations.

Fork bending

Ever wondered if you have psychic powers?
Fork benders try to move the prongs of a fork
using only their mind. It's never worked, though
(because psychic powers don't exist.) Shame!

YOUR FUTURE CAREER

Imagine if one of your favourite things to do became your career!
Draw what you'd be doing as a grown-up - it could be writing, sports,
teaching, painting, building, making TV, or anything else you love!

Where would your work take place? In an office, stadium, race track, art studio, or kitchen?

How do you look different as a grown-up?

What would you be wearing?

What tools would you need?

NAME:

....

AGE (choose a grown-up age):

....

CAREER:

....

ACHIEVEMENTS:

....

HOBBY-MATIC MACHINE

Design a machine to do a favourite hobby for you. It can have mechanical arms or legs - or perhaps it prints things out, or cooks things, or sculpts them? Can it speak, or travel fast? It's up to you...

Title: THE MARVELOUS

....

MACHINE

**Write what would happen
if your machine went wrong!**

....

....

....

....

....

....

A WORLD OF FUN!

Practice makes perfect - so whatever you love to do, make sure you keep doing it. There's no limit to what you can do, if it's something you love!

WHY NOT TRY...

Show others what you love! Set up a
performace of your music, or reading
something you've written, or an exhibition
of the art you've made. It might inspire
others to have a go too.

PART 6

BE YOUR BEST

YOU CAN DO ANYTHING!

There's nothing stopping you from getting to your dream goals – as long as you put in the time and effort to get there. Here's how to visualise your way to a better you!

MY BEST MOMENT

Let's start by visualising your goal.
Draw yourself in your ultimate
awesome moment - it could be you
now, or you in the future!

What I'm doing:

....

....

Skills I learned to get here:

....

....

Where it's happening:

....

....

To get here, I need to:

....

....

LEAVE YOUR COMFORT ZONE

An easy way to achieve your goals is to swap out an easy activity for something that's a bit tougher - or something you've never tried before! The first two are filled in for you to give you some ideas...

Comfort zone   ## Awesome zone

Sitting on the sofa   ······▶   **Getting up and running**
playing on a tablet   **round the block**

Staying talking to the   ······▶   **Saying 'hi' to that one**
mates I know   **person I see every day**
                                                   but never speak to

---

······▶

······▶

······▶

······▶

"DUDE, SUCKING AT SOMETHING IS THE FIRST STEP TO BEING SORTA GOOD AT SOMETHING"

JAKE THE DOG
Adventure Time

MY HERO

Draw and describe somebody you'd love to be like. It could be a friend or family member, or even a fictional character!

Name:
....

Best at:
....

Skills:
....

Hero tools:
....

When something bad happens, my hero does this:
....
....

I can be like them by doing this:
....
....

THE PATH TO VICTORY

It's time to choose a goal and plan how to get there.
Fill in the boxes to give yourself a path to victory!

1. Set your goal

Set your goal here. It could be:

- Improving your school work
- Learning a new sport
- Winning a match
- Saving some money
- Improving your fitness

Or something completely different!

Write it here:

....
....
....
....

2. Laser focus

Now it's time to focus right down on what you want, and by when. Be specfic! That will make it much easier to measure how well you're doing.

By (insert date here):

....

I will have:

....
....
....
....

3. Kick off

Getting started can be the hardest part. Give yourself a mini-prize for getting the first part of your task done. It could be a snack, a break or just giving yourself a pat on the back!

When I have:

....

I will reward myself with:

....
....

GOAL

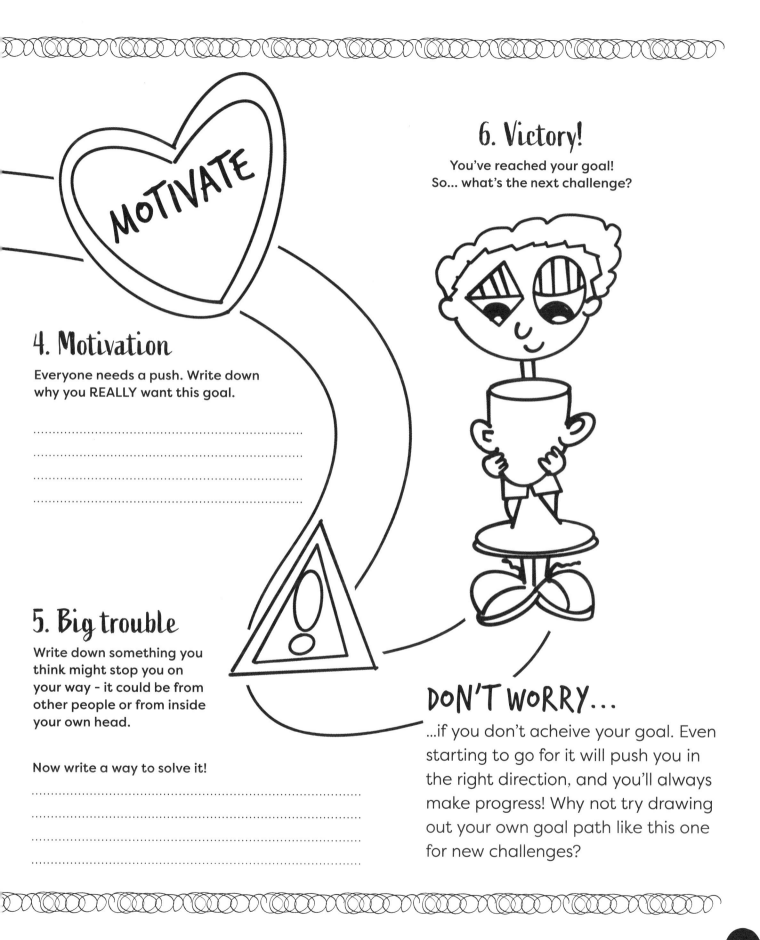

MOTIVATE

6. Victory!

You've reached your goal!
So... what's the next challenge?

4. Motivation

Everyone needs a push. Write down
why you REALLY want this goal.

....

....

....

....

5. Big trouble

Write down something you
think might stop you on
your way - it could be from
other people or from inside
your own head.

Now write a way to solve it!

....

....

....

....

DON'T WORRY...

...if you don't acheive your goal. Even
starting to go for it will push you in
the right direction, and you'll always
make progress! Why not try drawing
out your own goal path like this one
for new challenges?

IMPOSSIBLE DREAMS

Forget about everyday goals for a bit!
Use this space to draw those dreams
that seem completely impossible.

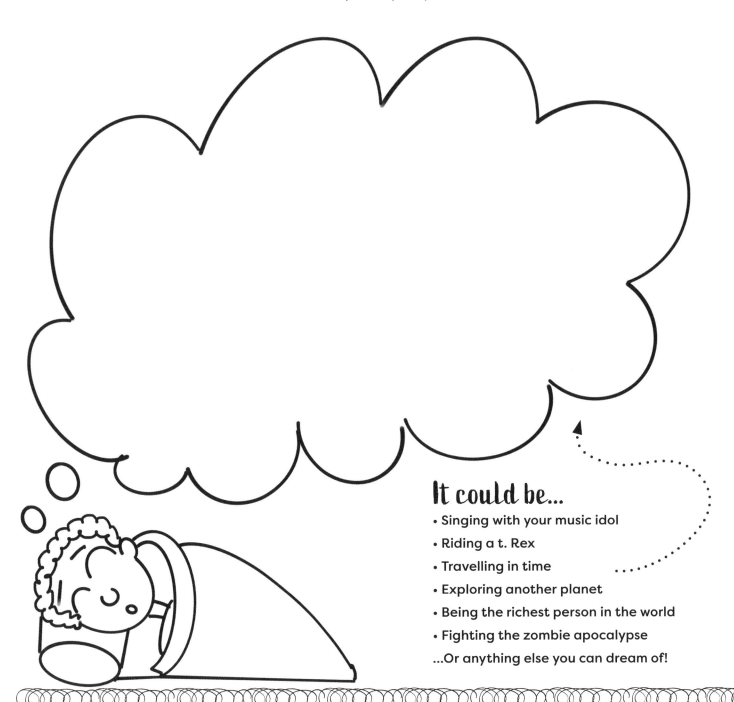

It could be...

- Singing with your music idol
- Riding a t. Rex
- Travelling in time
- Exploring another planet
- Being the richest person in the world
- Fighting the zombie apocalypse

...Or anything else you can dream of!

TRY SOMETHING NEW

Why not start something you've never tried before? Choose one COMPLETELY NEW activity in each of the groups.

Sport

This would be great because...

....

....

I've never tried it because....

....

....

I can try it if I...

....

....

School subject $20 \div 4$

This would be great because...

....

....

I've never tried it because....

....

....

I can try it if I...

....

....

Performance (like music, acting, presenting)

This would be great because...

....

....

I've never tried it because....

....

....

I can try it if I...

....

....

SCHOOL CONCERT

ANYTHING IS POSSIBLE!

It's time to jump right out of your comfort zone and
do something new - there's no limit to what you
can achieve if you try!

WHY NOT TRY...

All the greatest people failed on their way to the top. Make a list of some of the times you've messed up... and then add what you've learned from each time. It sounds weird, but you've got to rack up those failures to get awesome at anything!

PART 7

SPEAK OUT

MAKE YOURSELF SEEN!

Did the world ever make you mad, or sad, or upset
at how unfair something is? Art is the perfect way
to express yourself - and make a change!

MAKING A BETTER PLACE

What issues matter to you?

Draw the global issue you care about most here! It could do with helping animals, the environment or people in need... it's up to you.

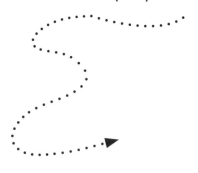

CLOSER TO HOME

It's okay to start small. Is there something in your everyday life that you think is unfair? It could be something at school, home or in the local community. Do others think the same way?

Draw a plan of your area, including your home, your school and some places you shop and play. . . . .

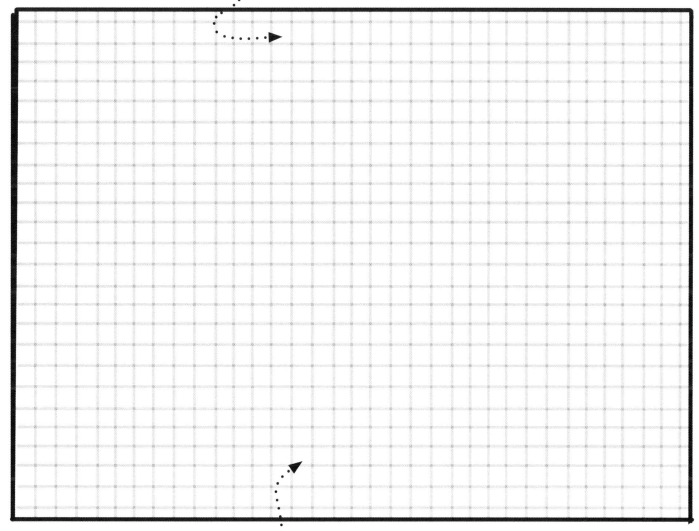

Colour the fairer places in blues and greens, and the less fair places in hot reds, oranges and yellows. . . . . .

"Any form of art is a form of power; it has impact, it can affect change"

OSSIE DAVIS
Actor and director

TAKE 2

INFLUENCER APPEAL

Everyone's an influencer! Write down some of the people you speak to or see every day. You'll be surprised how many others might hear your message.

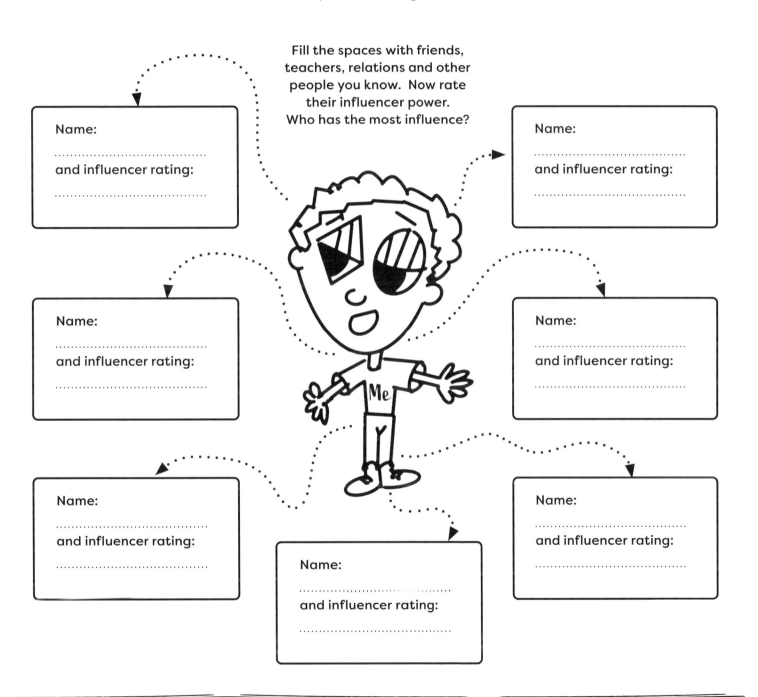

Fill the spaces with friends, teachers, relations and other people you know. Now rate their influencer power. Who has the most influence?

Name:
....
and influencer rating:
....

Name:
....
and influencer rating:
....

Name:
....
and influencer rating:
....

Name:
....
and influencer rating:
....

Name:
....
and influencer rating:
....

Name:
....
and influencer rating:
....

Name:
....
and influencer rating:
....

CHANGE MAKERS

Take a look at this gallery of heroes who weren't afraid to speak out. Now add some from your own personal list! They can be historical people, people you've heard about, or change makers from your own life who never stop trying to make things better.

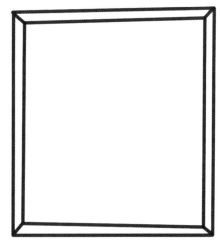

NAME: ....

ACHIEVEMENTS: ....

....

....

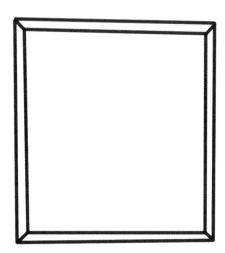

NAME: ....

ACHIEVEMENTS: ....

....

....

Martin Luther King Jr.

ACHIEVEMENTS: Spoke out for civil rights, triggering a massive change in the US in the 1960s.

QUOTE: "If you can't fly then run, if you can't run then walk, if you can't walk then crawl, but whatever you do you have to keep moving forward."

NAME: ....

ACHIEVEMENTS: ....

....

....

Malala Yousafzai

ACHIEVEMENTS: Campaigns for women's equality worldwide.

QUOTE: "We realise the importance of our voices only when we are silenced."

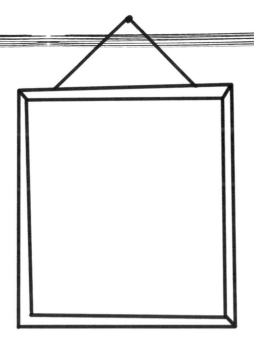

NAME:
....
ACHIEVEMENTS:
....
....
....

NAME:
....
ACHIEVEMENTS:
....
....
....

Ai Weiwei

ACHIEVEMENTS: Has used his art to criticise oppressive governments.

QUOTE: "I think art is a very important weapon to achieve human freedom."

CREATE A POSTER

Choose an issue that's close to you.
It could be something at school,
home or in society.

Use large words to get
your point across in a short
slogan – make it a call to
action, to get something
done NOW!

Come up with a
symbol for your
cause - or maybe
a picture to show
what's happening.

When you've finished your poster,
copy it or remove it from this book,
and display it somewhere everyone
will see it.

Explain what the
problem is and what
needs to be done -
keep it snappy so it's
easy to read!

GET YOUR MESSAGE OUT!

When you've created your poster on the previous page, imagine how you could add it to this scene. Your message could be on walls, posters, placards and even TV!

Write a slogan for a placard!

Add yourself on TV talking to the world!

Draw your cool poster here!

ART... JUST FOR YOU

Sometimes it's good to get your message out there. But don't forget - it's fine if you create art that's only for you to see, and nobody else.

Use this space to draw something that's important to you, and that nobody else ever needs to see or understand.

If you want to keep it really private, draw it on a separate piece of paper, and keep it safe... or even throw it away after you've drawn it. It's making the art that counts - what you do with it is completely up to you!

MAKE A CHANGE!

It's okay to have strong feelings about subjects you care deeply about - you might feel sad, angry, excited or frustrated. Talking to other people when you feel like this can be really helpful!

WHY NOT TRY...

If something is going on in your community, country or the world that upsets you, then share it! Maybe some of your friends feel the same as you and will want to do something about it. Think of creative ways to spread the message. Doing something together could make a real difference!

+ — + — + — + —

PART 8

LET IT ALL OUT...
ON PAPER

EXPRESS YOUR FEELINGS!

What happens when your feelings are too big to contain?
Whether they're positive or negative, turning them into
amazing art can really help. Here's how...

COLOUR MY FEELINGS

Use this space to add different colours, and think about how they make you feel. Do different colours conjure up different emotions for you?

Red

reminds me of:

....

Makes me feel:

....

Blue

reminds me of:

....

Makes me feel:

....

Green

reminds me of:

....

Makes me feel:

....

Black

reminds me of:

....

Makes me feel:

....

Yellow

reminds me of:

....

Makes me feel:

....

RAGE IT OUT!

Feeling ANGRY? Use this space to scrawl, scratch, and scribble out your feelings. Use whatever pen, pencil or paint you've got to hand. No need for any arty shapes or colours here. Just go crazy!

Hey, calm down!
You'll rip the page.
JUST KIDDING –
GO FOR IT!

CALMING MANDALAS

Have you ever tried drawing a mandala? It's an aid to medition in some religions. Drawing a mandala can promote feelings of calm and peace. Why not give it a try...

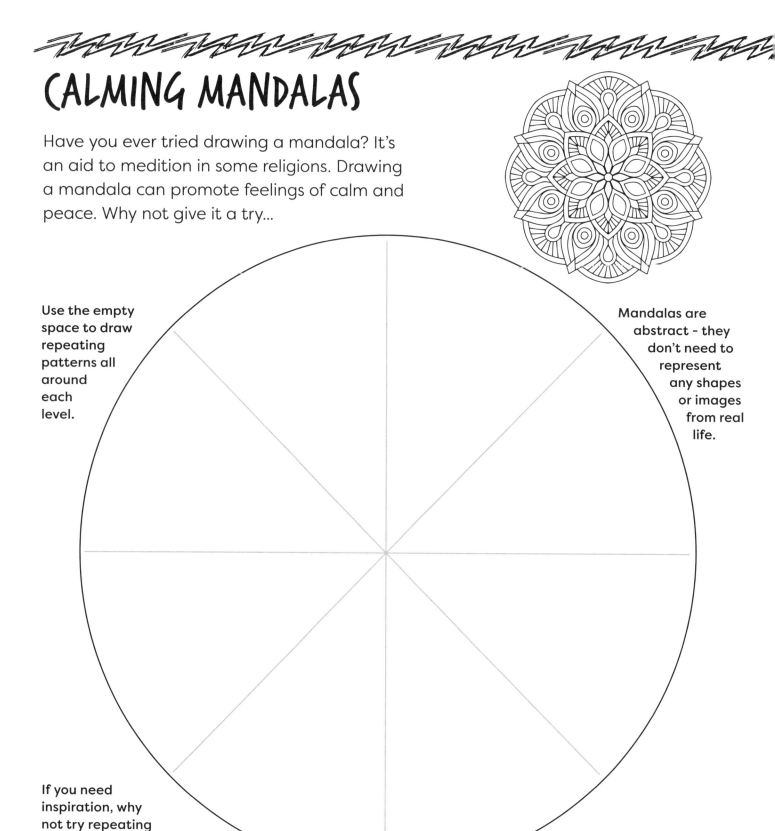

Use the empty space to draw repeating patterns all around each level.

Mandalas are abstract - they don't need to represent any shapes or images from real life.

If you need inspiration, why not try repeating letter or number shapes around the patterns?

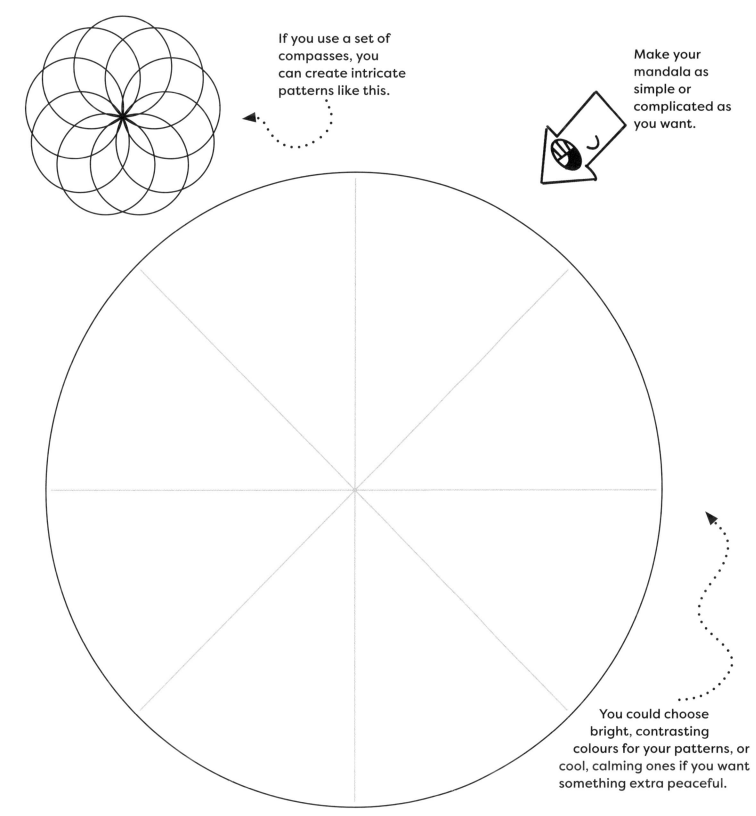

If you use a set of compasses, you can create intricate patterns like this.

Make your mandala as simple or complicated as you want.

You could choose bright, contrasting colours for your patterns, or cool, calming ones if you want something extra peaceful.

"If ART doesn't make us BETTER, then what on EARTH is it for?"

ALICE WALKER
Writer

FACE YOUR FEARS

Try drawing three things that make you scared, angry or upset. They could be people or situations. Once you've drawn them... add something to make them funny, to take away the fear. The sillier the better!

Scared of being alone? Add some fun imaginary friends!

You could make scary grown-ups look like tiny babies!

My fear:

....

i made it funny by:

....

....

....

Monster hiding under your bed? Give it a fantastic sparkly makeover!

MY PERFECT ROOM

Design your own perfect room -
the place where you can feel most
comfortable and safe.

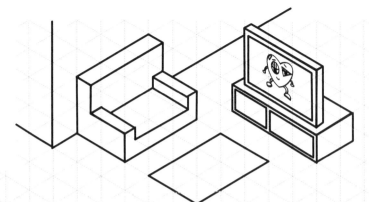

What's on the wall? Posters? Bookshelves? Decorations? Photos?

What sports equipment, toys or computers would you have?

You can add anything you like in
your fantasy room. Robot butler?
Climbing wall? Pet dragon? Shark
tank? It's up to you!

Add a bed and
bedsheets in a
cool design.

ART FOR EVERY HEART

Art can move you, or move others. It can calm you or fire you up - it can help you work out who you are, or what you want to do. You've got a world of art inside you - so get it out there and show everyone!

WHY NOT TRY...

Remember - all the ideas in this book
are just jumping-off points for your own
projects. So why not try mashing them up,
swapping them round, or redoing ones you
enjoy on spare paper. You could challenge
a friend to do them with you too. And
whatever you do - put your heart into it!